La volpe e la gru

Favola di Esopo

The Fox and the Crane

An Aesop's Fable

retold by Dawn Casey

illustrated by Jago

Italian translation by Michela Masci

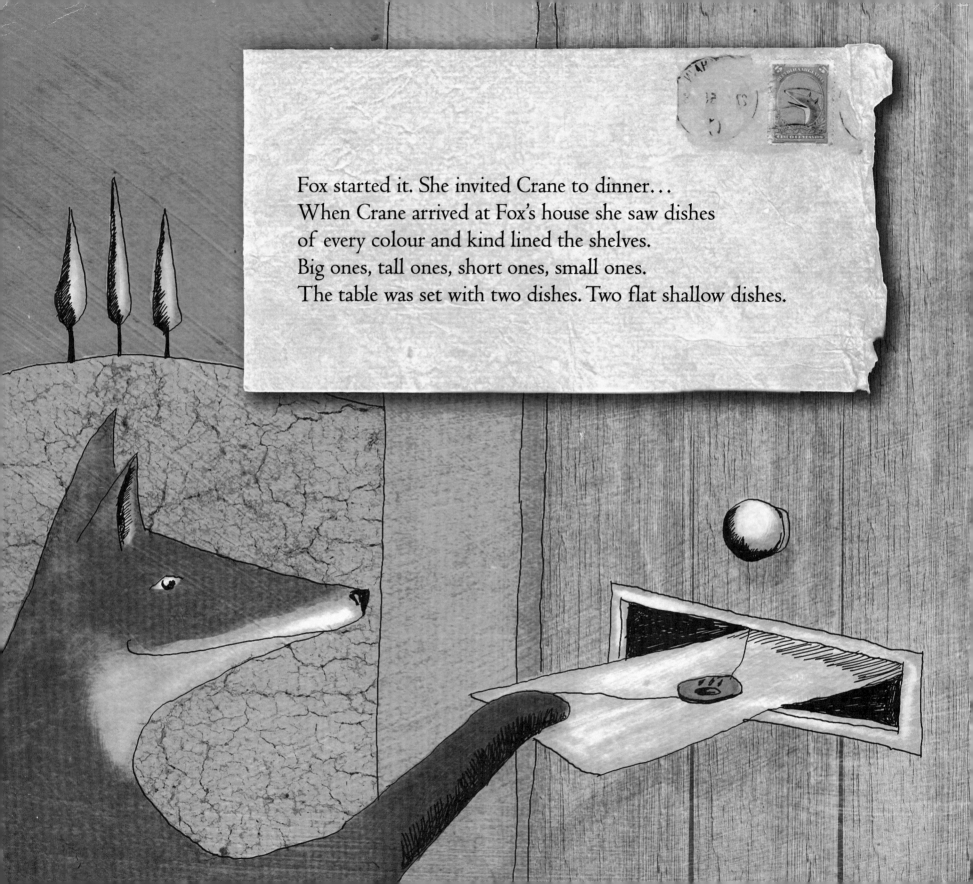

Fox started it. She invited Crane to dinner…
When Crane arrived at Fox's house she saw dishes
of every colour and kind lined the shelves.
Big ones, tall ones, short ones, small ones.
The table was set with two dishes. Two flat shallow dishes.

Fu la volpe a cominciare. Invitò a cena la gru...
Quando la gru arrivò a casa della volpe, vide in bella mostra
sulla credenza stoviglie di ogni colore e di ogni tipo: grandi,
alte, basse, piccole. La tavola era apparecchiata per due.
Con due piatti piani.

La gru beccava e cercava di prendere la minestra con il lungo becco sottile, ma, per quanto si sforzasse, non riusciva a berne neppure un sorso.

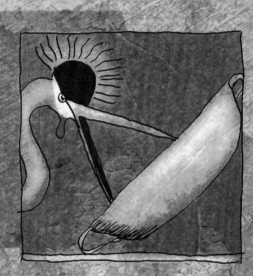

Crane pecked and she picked with her long thin beak. But no matter how hard she tried she could not get even a sip of the soup.

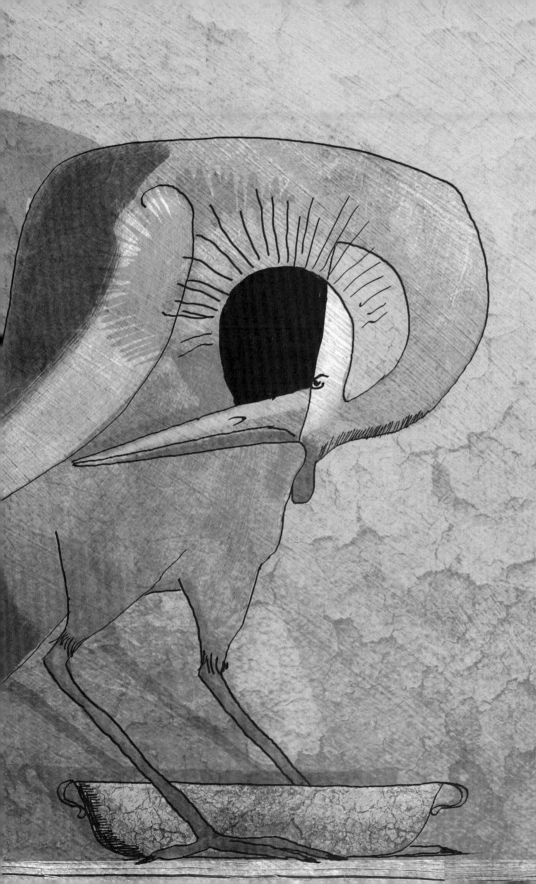

La volpe osservava le difficoltà della gru e ridacchiava. Sollevò la sua minestra fino alle labbra e, SIP, SLOP, SLURP, se la leccò tutta. "Ahhhh, ottima!" disse in tono di scherno, asciugandosi i baffi col dorso della zampa.
"Oh gru, non hai ancora toccato la minestra", disse la volpe con un sorrisetto. "Davvero mi DISPIACE che non ti sia piaciuta", aggiunse, cercando di non ridere troppo.

Fox watched Crane struggling and sniggered. She lifted her own soup to her lips, and with a SIP, SLOP, SLURP she lapped it all up.
"Ahhhh, delicious!" she scoffed, wiping her whiskers with the back of her paw.
"Oh Crane, you haven't touched your soup," said Fox with a smirk. "I AM sorry you didn't like it," she added, trying not to snort with laughter.

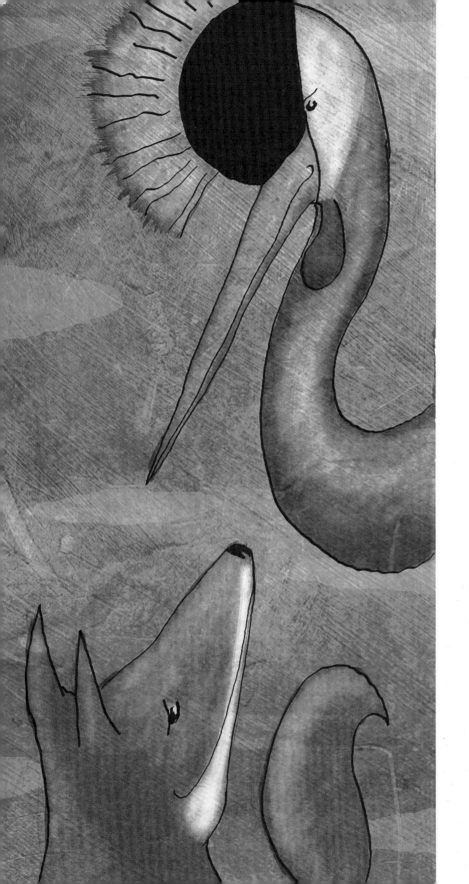

La gru non disse niente. Guardò la cena. Guardò il piatto. Guardò la volpe e sorrise.
"Cara volpe, ti ringrazio per la gentilezza", disse la gru cortesemente. "Permettimi, ti prego, di ricambiare: vieni a cena da me."

Quando la volpe arrivò, la finestra era aperta e ne usciva un profumino delizioso. La volpe sollevò il muso e annusò. Aveva l'acquolina in bocca e le brontolava lo stomaco. Si leccò le labbra.

Crane said nothing. She looked at the meal. She looked at the dish. She looked at Fox, and smiled.
"Dear Fox, thank you for your kindness," said Crane politely. "Please let me repay you – come to dinner at my house."

When Fox arrived the window was open. A delicious smell drifted out. Fox lifted her snout and sniffed. Her mouth watered. Her stomach rumbled. She licked her lips.

"Mia cara volpe, entra pure", disse la gru,
allargando le ali con grazia.
La volpe passò, dandole una spinta.
Vide in bella mostra sulla credenza
stoviglie di ogni colore e di ogni tipo:
rosse, blu, vecchie, nuove.
La tavola era apparecchiata per due.
Con due vasi alti e stretti.

"My dear Fox, do come in," said Crane,
extending her wing graciously.
Fox pushed past. She saw dishes of
every colour and kind lined the shelves.
Red ones, blue ones, old ones, new ones.
The table was set with two dishes.
Two tall narrow dishes.

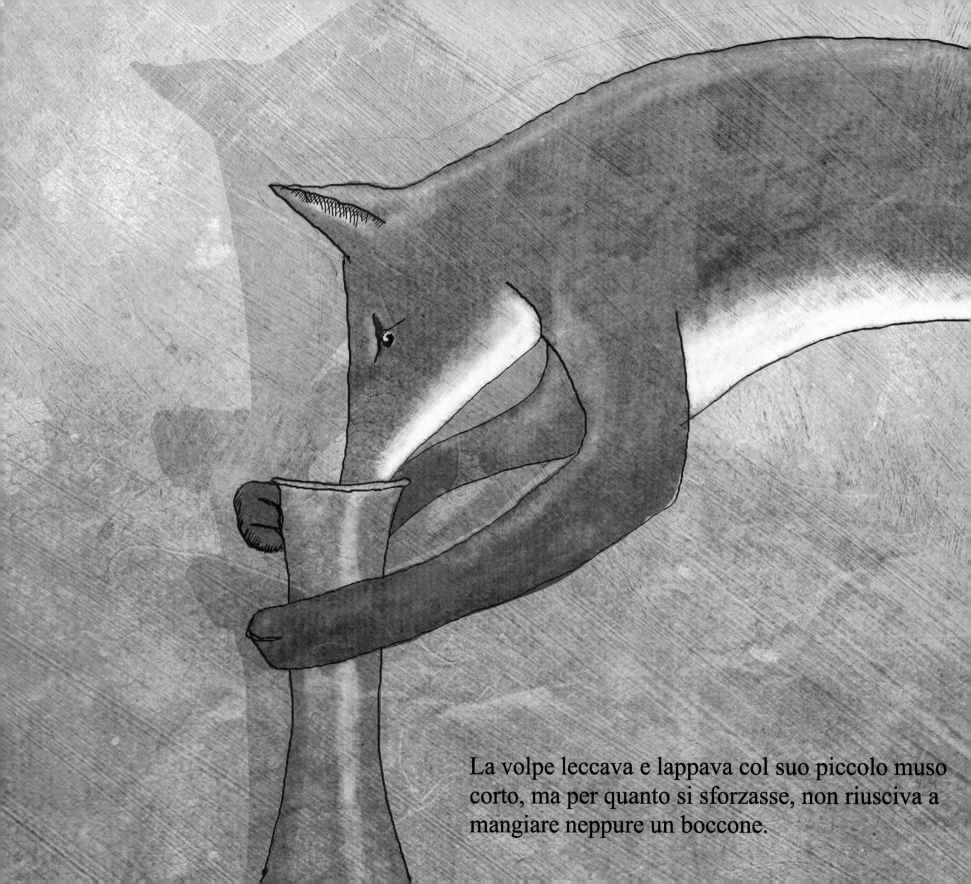

La volpe leccava e lappava col suo piccolo muso corto, ma per quanto si sforzasse, non riusciva a mangiare neppure un boccone.

Fox licked and she lapped with her short little snout.
But no matter how hard she tried she could not
get even a mouthful of the meal.

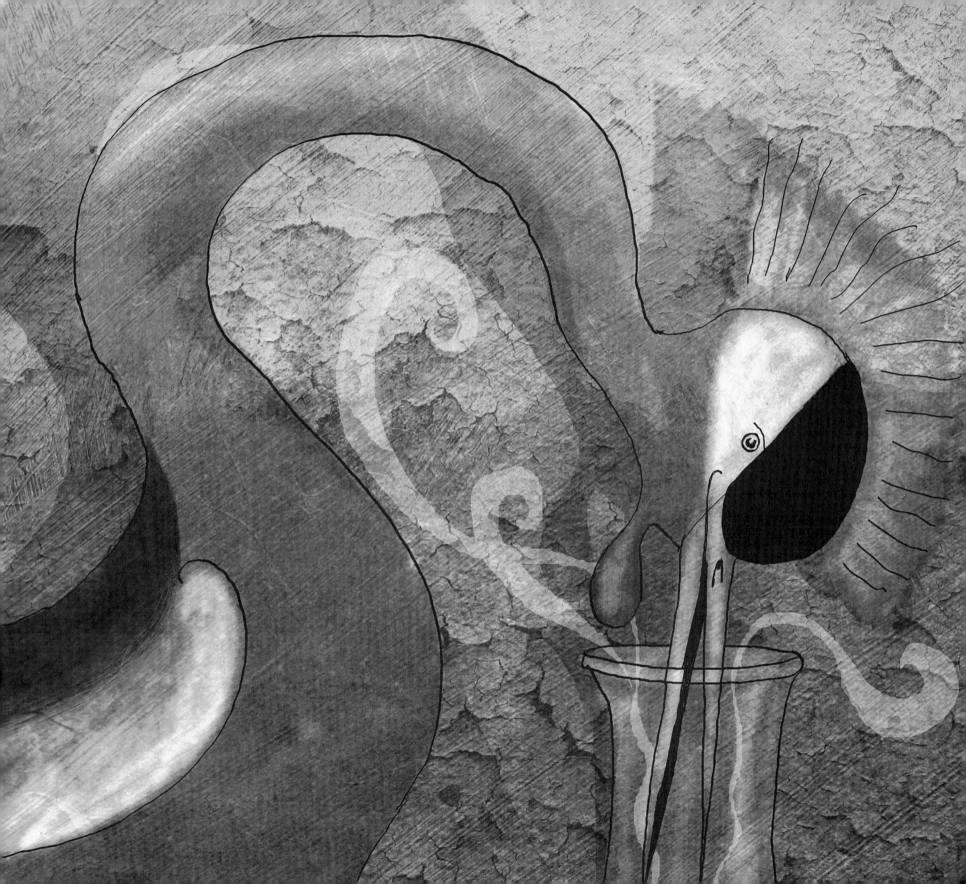

La gru mangiò molto lentamente, assaporando ogni boccone.
"Cara volpe, ti ringrazio tanto per essere venuta", disse
sorridendo, "è stato un piacere restituirti la gentilezza."

La pancia della volpe gorgogliava e brontolava.
Quando tornò a casa aveva ancora fame.

Crane ate her meal very slowly, savouring every mouthful.
"Dear Fox, thank you so much for coming," she smiled,
"it has been a pleasure to repay your kindness."

Fox's tummy gurgled and grumbled.
And when she went home, she was still hungry.

The Fox and the Crane

Writing Activity:
Read the story. Explain that we can write our own fable by changing the characters.

Discuss the different animals you could use, bearing in mind what different kinds of dishes they would need! For example, instead of the fox and the crane you could have a tiny mouse and a tall giraffe.

Write an example together as a class, then give the children the opportunity to write their own. Children who need support could be provided with a writing frame.

Art Activity:
Dishes of every colour and kind! Create them from clay, salt dough, play dough… Make them, paint them, decorate them…

Maths Activity:
Provide a variety of vessels: bowls, jugs, vases, mugs… Children can use these to investigate capacity:

Compare the containers and order them from smallest to largest.

Estimate the capacity of each container.

Young children can use non-standard measures e.g. 'about 3 beakers full'.

Check estimates by filling the container with coloured liquid ('soup') or dry lentils.

Older children can use standard measures such as a litre jug, and measure using litres and millilitres. How near were the estimates?

Label each vessel with its capacity.

The Ruler of the Forest

Writing Activity:
Children can write their own fables by changing the setting of this story. Think about what kinds of animals you would find in a different setting. For example how about 'The Ruler of the Arctic' starring an arctic fox and a polar bear!

Storytelling Activity:
Draw a long path down a roll of paper showing the route Fox took through the forest. The children can add their own details, drawing in the various scenes and re-telling the story orally with model animals.

If you are feeling ambitious you could chalk the path onto the playground so that children can act out the story using appropriate noises and movements! (They could even make masks to wear, decorated with feathers, woollen fur, sequin scales etc.)

Music Activity:
Children choose a forest animal. Then select an instrument that will make a sound that matches the way their animal looks and moves. Encourage children to think about musical features such as volume, pitch and rhythm. For example a loud, low, plodding rhythm played on a drum could represent an elephant.

Children perform their animal sounds. Can the class guess the animal?

Children can play their pieces in groups, to create a forest soundscape.

La Sovrana della foresta
Favola cinese

The Ruler of the Forest
A Chinese Fable

retold by Dawn Casey

illustrated by Jago

Italian translation by Michela Masci

La volpe camminava nella foresta, quando sentì qualcosa muoversi tra l'erba alta.

RUSTLE   Qualcosa di grande.
BLINK   Qualcosa dagli occhi gialli.
FLASH   Qualcosa dai denti come coltelli.

Fox was walking in the forest when she heard something moving in the long grass.

RUSTLE   Something big.
BLINK   Something with yellow eyes.
FLASH   Something with teeth like knives.

"Buongiorno, piccola volpe", salutò la tigre con un gran sorriso. La sua bocca era tutta denti.

La volpe deglutì.

"Che piacere incontrarti", disse la tigre facendo le fusa, "stavo giusto cominciando ad avere fame."

La volpe si fece venire un'idea alla svelta. "Come osi!" disse. "Non sai che sono la sovrana della foresta?"

"Tu! Sovrana della foresta?" disse la tigre e rise ruggendo.

"Se non mi credi", rispose la volpe con dignità, "cammina dietro di me e vedrai: tutti hanno paura di me."

"Voglio proprio vedere", disse la tigre.

Così la volpe si mise a passeggiare per la foresta. La tigre la seguiva con fierezza, tenendo la coda alta, fino a che...

"Good morning little fox," Tiger grinned, and her mouth was nothing but teeth.

Fox gulped.

"I am pleased to meet you," Tiger purred. "I was just beginning to feel hungry."

Fox thought fast. "How dare you!" she said. "Don't you know I'm the Ruler of the Forest?"

"You! Ruler of the Forest?" said Tiger, and she roared with laughter.

"If you don't believe me," replied Fox with dignity, "walk behind me and you'll see — everyone is scared of me."

"This I've got to see," said Tiger.

So Fox strolled through the forest. Tiger followed behind proudly, with her tail held high, until...

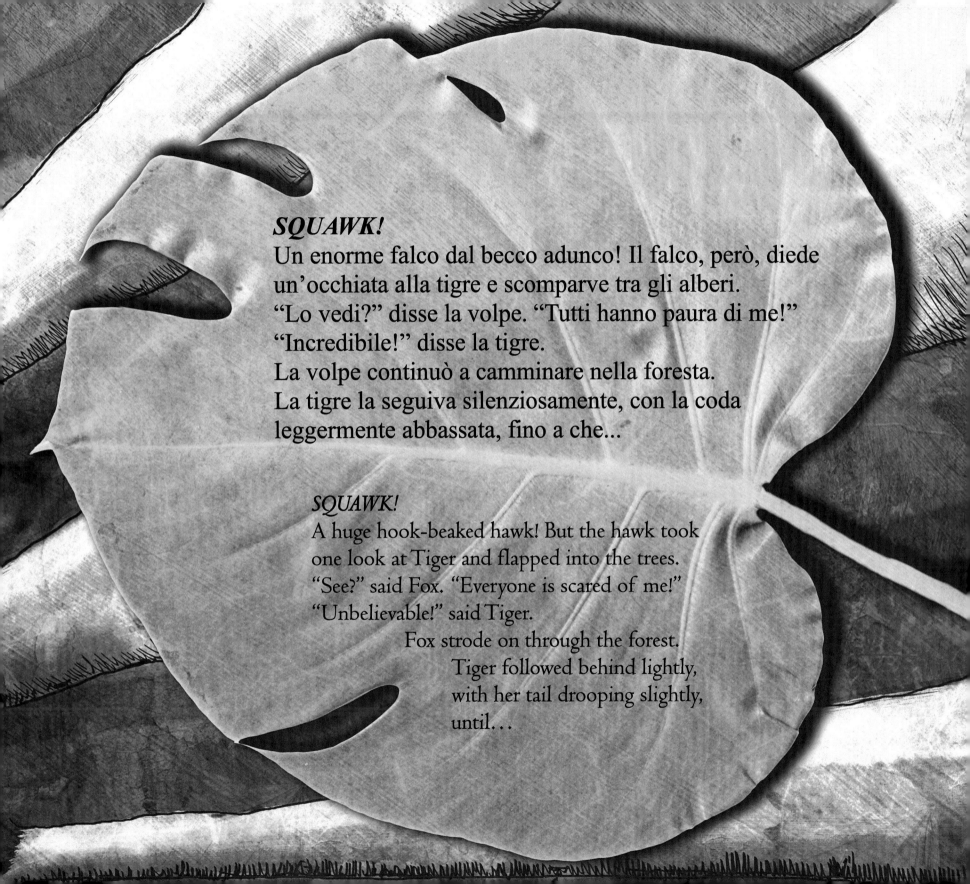

SQUAWK!
Un enorme falco dal becco adunco! Il falco, però, diede
un'occhiata alla tigre e scomparve tra gli alberi.
"Lo vedi?" disse la volpe. "Tutti hanno paura di me!"
"Incredibile!" disse la tigre.
La volpe continuò a camminare nella foresta.
La tigre la seguiva silenziosamente, con la coda
leggermente abbassata, fino a che...

SQUAWK!
A huge hook-beaked hawk! But the hawk took
one look at Tiger and flapped into the trees.
"See?" said Fox. "Everyone is scared of me!"
"Unbelievable!" said Tiger.
Fox strode on through the forest.
Tiger followed behind lightly,
with her tail drooping slightly,
until…

GROWL!

Un grande orso nero! L'orso, però, diede un'occhiata
alla tigre e si infilò nei cespugli.
"Lo vedi?" disse la volpe. "Tutti hanno paura di me!"
"Incredibile!" disse la tigre.
La volpe continuò ad avanzare nella foresta. La tigre
la seguiva docilmente, trascinando la coda per terra,
fino a che...

GROWL!

A big black bear! But the bear took one look
at Tiger and crashed into the bushes.
"See?" said Fox. "Everyone is scared of me!"
"Incredible!" said Tiger.
Fox marched on through the forest. Tiger
followed behind meekly, with her tail
dragging on the forest floor, until…

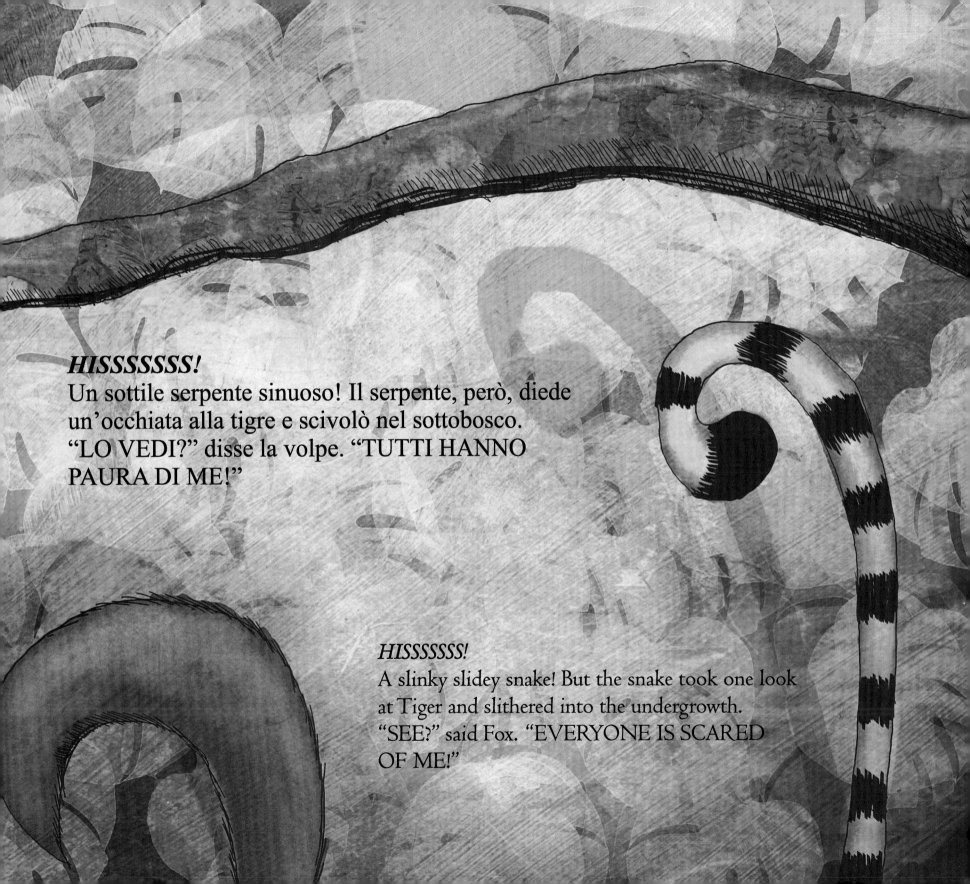

HISSSSSSS!
Un sottile serpente sinuoso! Il serpente, però, diede un'occhiata alla tigre e scivolò nel sottobosco.
"LO VEDI?" disse la volpe. "TUTTI HANNO PAURA DI ME!"

HISSSSSSS!
A slinky slidey snake! But the snake took one look at Tiger and slithered into the undergrowth.
"SEE?" said Fox. "EVERYONE IS SCARED OF ME!"

"Lo vedo", disse la tigre, "tu sei la sovrana della foresta e io sono la tua umile servitrice."

"Bene", disse la volpe. "Allora sparisci!"

E la tigre se ne andò, con la coda tra le zampe.

"I do see," said Tiger, "you are the Ruler of the Forest and I am your humble servant."
"Good," said Fox. "Then, be gone!"

And Tiger went, with her tail between her legs.

"Sovrana della foresta", si disse la volpe con un sorriso. Il sorriso si allargò e poi si trasformò in una risatina, e la volpe rise a squarciagola fino a casa.

"Ruler of the Forest," said Fox to herself with a smile. Her smile grew into a grin, and her grin grew into a giggle, and Fox laughed out loud all the way home.

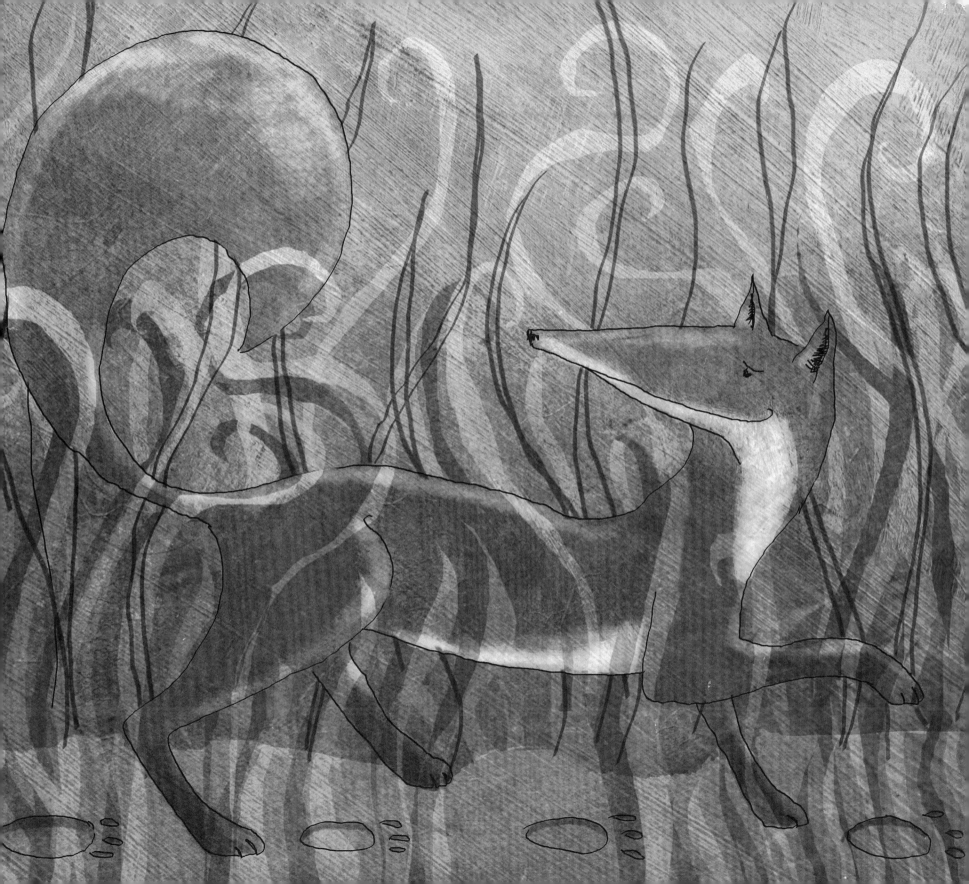

To my Nana, with love ~ DC

For my wife, Alex ~ J

First published in 2006 by Mantra Lingua Ltd
Global House, 303 Ballards Lane
London N12 8NP
www.mantralingua.com

Text copyright © 2006 Dawn Casey
Illustration copyright © 2006 Jago
Dual language copyright © 2006 Mantra Lingua Ltd
This edition 2012

A CIP record for this book is available from the British Library